**COLLINS GEM**
**CATS**
*a mine of information*

**COLLINS GEM**
**HORSES** & PONIES
*a mine of information*

**COLLINS GEM**
**INSECTS**
*a mine of information*

**COLLINS GEM**
**KINGS &**
**QUEENS**
*a mine of information*

**COLLINS GEM**
& TOADSTOOLS
*a mine of information*

**COLLINS GEM**
**SNAKES**
*a mine of information*

**COLLINS GEM**
**SPIDERS**
*a mine of information*

**COLLINS GEM**
**STRESS**
Survival Guide
*a mine of information*

**COLLINS GEM**
**TAROT**
*a mine of information*

**COLLINS GEM**
**WINE**
Guide
*a mine of information*

**COLLINS GEM**
**WORLD**
**atlas**
*a mine of information*

**COLLINS GEM**
**YOGA**
*a mine of information*

**COLLINS GEM**
**ZODIAC**
Types
*a mine of information*

C000297729

# TAI CHI

**Ronnie Robinson**

HarperCollins*Publishers*

The right of Ronnie Robinson to be identified as the author of this work has been asserted by him in accordance with the Copyright, Designs and Patents Act 1988

HarperCollins*Publishers*
Westerhill Road, Bishopbriggs, Glasgow G64 2QT

First published 2001

Reprint 10 9 8 7 6 5 4 3 2 1 0

© Essential Books 2001
Photographs © Gary Ombler

ISBN 0 00 711013-8

Printed in Italy by Amadeus S.p.A

# Contents

# Introduction

Early in the morning, in any park in any city in China, hundreds of people can be seen performing a series of slow, graceful movements. This is the art of Tai Chi, a respected and long-established communal tradition in one of the world's oldest cultures. What was originally developed as a martial art for self-defence has now become a highly effective exercise system that is practised and enjoyed by people of all ages.

This book is an introduction to the history, philosophy and practice of this fascinating, multifaceted art. It also introduces the various styles that are practised around the world today. More practically, it provides information on what can be expected when attending a regular Tai Chi class.

From its early origins in the holy Taoist mountains of China, to its growth as a form of physical meditation so much taken for granted as to have become a public custom, Tai Chi has emerged as a highly practical tool for life in the 21st century. Tai Chi can help to improve posture, increase energy levels and create a calm, clear mind. By learning a few simple postures, and regularly practising them for a few minutes each day, the practitioner can integrate this ancient Chinese system into his or her daily routine and enjoy its benefit in many ways: physically, mentally, emotionally and, ultimately, spiritually.

The principles of Tai Chi are at the heart of many other Chinese arts: traditional Chinese medicine, feng shui, Chinese astrology and the *I Ching* all use the concept as a model for creating harmony within our bodies and with our environment. By understanding the principles behind Tai Chi, practitioners find themselves better equipped for the practice of the art.

# WHAT IS TAI CHI?

*One becomes two and two becomes three and three becomes ten thousand things.*

The words 'Tai Chi' translate from the Chinese as 'supreme ultimate'. The supreme ultimate is the representation of the harmony and interrelationship of all things, best illustrated by the concepts of yin and yang. It is the connection between the two energies that creates new life and everything that comes from that. From this interchange of the two opposing yet complementary energies, everything else is created.

Tai Chi Ch'uan is a Chinese exercise system which, although originally developed as a martial art, can also be practised for health, relaxation and meditation. It involves a series of postures that are linked together to create a continuous flowing sequence of movement.

## TAI CHI CH'UAN

Although many people talk about 'Tai Chi', the words 'Tai Chi' only represent the concept outlined previously. It is just that – a concept or idea. One cannot practise an idea. We can apply this philosophical belief in our practice of the art, but it must be applied to doing something. What we practise is the art of Tai Chi Ch'uan. Today the exercise system is commonly referred to as Tai Chi (as it is in this book), but without its relationship to ch'uan it is nothing.

'Ch'uan' means 'fist' or 'boxing'. 'Tai Chi Ch'uan' therefore means 'supreme ultimate boxing'. This term always refers to a system of fighting that utilises the principles of Tai Chi. How the philosophy of Tai Chi is applied as a fighting art will be further explained in the section on partner work and martial applications.

# ORIGINS

Tai Chi is founded on theory and principles that go back thousands of years. Evidence of the concepts of yin and yang is found in the Yellow Emperor's *Classic of Huang Di*. This is the definitive classic of traditional Chinese medicine that, although written over 4,000 years ago, is still applied in acupuncture and Chinese herbalism and massage, and continues to play a role in healthcare today.

The art of Tai Chi can be traced back hundreds of years to the 13th-century Taoist sage Chang San-Feng. Legend has it that Chang San-Feng was over 6 ft (2 m) tall and a powerful fighter. It is said that he retired from his working life as a government official to further his spiritual development. He is reported to have trained in Shaolin boxing (a Chinese martial art developed by the Buddhist monks of the Shaolin Temple) before retreating to one of the holy mountains, Wudang Shan, to follow the *Tao* ('Way'). Shunning traditional monastery life, he preferred to live in a cave and spent his time in contemplation amid the beautiful natural

surroundings of these famous mountains.

For one who hoped to achieve harmony with nature, Chang San-Feng chose the perfect location on this sacred mountain. As well as beautifully inspiring peaks and rich vegetation, the area also contained over 400 kinds of Chinese herbs that are included in the *Materia Medica*, the ancient handbook for Chinese herbal remedies that is still in use today.

*An early doll used for the teaching of acupuncture. Acupoints are based along the meridians, which are central to Tai Chi*

According to legend, during one of his meditations Chang San-Feng observed a fight between a snake and a bird (a crane). When the crane dived to attack the snake, the snake slithered out of the way to avoid the bird's beak. When the snake rose up to spit its poison at the bird, the bird managed to spread its wings to defend itself. This fight went on for some time with no creature harming the other and each successfully avoiding the other's attacks. Chang San-Feng considered the natural flowing movements of these and other creatures and, together with his knowledge of Shaolin boxing, incorporated them into a series of exercises known as the Thirteen Postures.

The first system actually known as Tai Chi Ch'uan began in the 17th century in Chenjiagou village, Wenxian county, Henan, China. There Chen Wang-Ting began teaching, and from those teachings originated today's Tai Chi.

# PHILOSOPHY

# Yin and yang

The term 'Tai Chi' is represented by this symbol:

The symbol is a depiction of two aspects: yin and yang.

The white part is yang and the dark part is yin. The white part (yang) has a small black circle and the dark part (yin) has a small white circle. This represents the necessity that each aspect should also include part of its opposite aspect for things to be in balance.

The two aspects represent opposite yet complementary forces or energies. For example:

| Yang | Yin |
|------|-----|
| Sun | Moon |
| Day | Night |
| Hot | Cold |
| Summer | Winter |
| Hard | Soft |
| Active | Passive |
| Male | Female |
| Motion | Stillness |

Take a closer look at the Tai Chi symbol.

In observing the shape and form of the symbol, think about the concept of time. The point of extreme yin is when we have the darkest hour. Then, as the white part of yang appears, so too does dawn's early light. As time progresses, and the sun reaches its highest point, there is midday which is the extreme point of yang. Then as the day progresses the light slowly fades and the darkness or yin period begins.

In the yin period, there are still aspects of yang: there are stars and there is also the moon, which adds light to the sky, and amid the quiet resting period of night-time there is still activity in the heavens.

# Yin and yang and the four seasons

*There is nothing as constant as change.*

It is constant change, and our learning to adapt to it, that lies at the very heart of the practice of Tai Chi. One of the best ways of thinking about the relationship between yin and yang – principles that are central to Tai Chi – is by looking at how the seasons relate to each other.

In winter, when there is little growth, many of the creatures of the earth hibernate. This is a period of very little activity or yin. As the spring gradually awakens, the stirrings of new life and activity begin to appear: seeds begin to germinate and grow and lambs, rabbits and other creatures are born. In summer, when the sun is at its strongest, the flowers and plants are in full bloom. They have reached a stage when they can develop no more. Once this has been achieved, when the yang period (summer) has reached its extreme limit, the season of autumn arrives. Autumn is when old plants begin to die off and the seeds for new growth rest beneath the earth. In winter, as growth slows down and the nights get longer, the period of yin-ness, darkness and little activity commences. When this period nears its end the new yang period takes over once more and the beginnings of new growth emerge.

These two aspects of time and the seasons show that the nature of life is constantly in motion, regularly changing, gradually going through the aspects of yin and yang.

In movement there is yang activity and in stillness there is yin. Tai Chi is often referred to as 'stillness in motion'. On the outside the arms, legs, waist are moved, while the inside of the body (particularly the mind) remains quiet and still.

In performing the movements the limbs should never be overextended or locked. To lock the arms or legs is to create a position of extreme yang. This is potentially weak and dangerous. Only when extreme yang has been reached can a yin phase be entered. By pushing the arms as far forward as possible, and then a little more, a point is reached when the arms become weaker and have to be relaxed. This shows how the extreme of yang leads to yin and vice versa.

So contained within the Tai Chi symbol are equal amounts of yin and yang and within each aspect there is a little of the other. This symbol represents the ideal of harmony and balance. As the Tai Chi movements are performed, the aim should be to maintain harmony and balance in the body and its energy systems, which should, ideally, complement the harmony and balance found within the practitioner's external surroundings.

# Tai Chi and Taoism

Taoism is deeply connected to the philosophical belief that lies at the heart of the art of Tai Chi. Its earliest record is the *Tao-te ching*, traditionally ascribed to the famous sage Lao Tzu. Broadly, this is a system of thought that encourages taking a path of least resistance and living in harmony with one's

*Taoist temple on the southern face of the Wudang mountain*

surroundings. In certain branches of psychology there is a saying, 'Don't push the river'. This is a philosophy akin to the Taoist idea of 'going with the flow'. Essentially, what this means is that everything in the universe has its own 'way', or course of action, that it must take, and that there is nothing that can be done to oppose it. It is better to let things take their own natural course, goes the theory. This does not mean adopting a defeatist attitude, or being apathetic or inert, but rather realising that certain things must change, and that the forward movement cannot be stemmed. The Taoist accepts that change is inevitable and learns to make the most of that change.

The *Tao-te ching* is a series of texts that was attributed to someone referred to as Lao Tzu (which roughly translates as 'old master'). Whether Lao Tzu existed as one man or was a composite of many men is not certain, nor is it important. The words that were left under this authorship carry meaning and resonance of deep relevance, not only many centuries ago when they were written, but also in today's stressful society.

The exact meaning of these paradoxically simple yet profound words is not entirely clear, nor is it meant to be. For example:

> *The Tao that can be spoken of is not the true Tao.*

and

> *The Tao that can be known is not known.*
> *Empty and be full;*
> *Wear out and be new;*
> *Have little and gain.*

Lao Tzu goes on to say:

> *The softest thing in the universe*
> *overcomes the hardest thing in the universe.*

These simple words help the Taoist to realise that there is a way of achieving success that does not require constant struggle. If a physical (or mental) attack is greeted with a strong, rigid (full) defence (again in body or mind), attack results. If, however, the attack is treated with lightness (or emptiness) there is the opportunity to yield to the force while still maintaining a central and balanced position.

The writings also help to illustrate the nature of those who truly apply the philosophy of martial arts, not just as a guide to combat but also as a guide for living:

> *Whosoever knows how to lead well*
> *Is not warlike,*
>
> *Whosoever knows how to fight well*
> *Is not angry,*
>
> *Whosoever knows how to conquer enemies*
> *Does not fight them,*
>
> *Whosoever knows how to use men well,*
> *Keeps himself below.*

# Internal energy

## CHI

In Chinese belief, *chi* is the very essence of life. Not only is it found in the air that we breathe but it is also the vital energy of the body.

Inside the body there are a series of pathways or 'meridians' that carry this internal *chi* energy. Each meridian is connected to an internal organ and feeds the energy system of that organ. The meridians can be thought of as rivers where the energy flows. When a river flows regularly, everything within it is fresh and healthy. If the river becomes stagnant, very soon life within it starts to rot or decay. It is important for people to ensure the smooth flow of energy in the rivers or meridians of their bodies. Along the meridians there are a series of acupoints where needles can be inserted to regulate the flow of energy in order to treat a particular problem. The practice of Tai Chi encourages this energy flow by combining movements, breath and mental focus.

According to the principles behind Tai Chi, human beings are born with a certain amount of energy in their bodies. This is referred to as pre-natal *chi*, and people are given a limited supply. Levels of post-natal *chi* can be increased, however. This increase can be achieved in a number of ways. *Chi* can be obtained from food, drink and exercise. Conversely, supplies of post-natal *chi* can be negatively affected by over-eating, drinking too much or by indulging in an excessive lifestyle.

Tai Chi exercises help to promote the flow of internal *chi* energy in the body. The pupil should concentrate on maintaining mindful awareness (*yi*) or focus during practice, and combining this with smooth, fluid movements and natural, soft breathing. Together these elements form the best conditions for the development of the body's natural healing energies.

When practising Tai Chi, the arms, legs and waist are moved. By moving the body, muscle groups are exercised. If this were all that happened it would be the same as any other form of exercise. It is important when practising to focus the mind – *yi* – on the sequences of movement. By focusing on the execution of a posture or movement, and by paying attention to the purpose of the movement, the internal *chi* energy is also stimulated throughout the meridians.

When Chang San-Feng developed the original Thirteen Postures that were to become Tai Chi, he combined his knowledge of yin/yang and Five

Elemental theory (*see page 48*) with that of traditional Chinese medicine. Added to these was his awareness of internal energy (*chi*). Together these formed a system for self-defence and physical and mental wellbeing, which allowed the body to increase its natural healing energy and find its optimum state of harmony and balance.

*According to Chinese tradition, Tai Chi promotes the flow of energy (or 'chi') through pathways (or 'meridians') in the body*

# RECOGNISED SYSTEMS OF TAI CHI

Traditionally, in China and the Far East, martial arts were closely guarded secrets that were practised predominantly in close-knit family groups. At a time when the majority of people worked in manual labour, if someone possessed a unique skill then they could often ensure a better living standard for their family. In these days a skilled craftsman would traditionally pass his art through to his children, as was often seen with generations of craftsmen such as silversmiths and blacksmiths. If an individual was a skilled fighter they could not only defend themselves against any potential attacker, but also gain well-paid employment working to defend those who had precious resources that they were eager to protect.

Although there are a number of variations of the original style of Tai Chi, all recognised styles can be traced to an authenticated lineage and adhere to certain principles. As with any art form, popularity spawns many imitations, and ultimately the art is in danger of becoming something greatly different from what it started out to be. While one of the inherent beliefs at the heart of Tai Chi philosophy is the constancy of change, it is the effectiveness of the principles that make Tai Chi what it is.

Anyone with a mind to enter the world of Tai Chi has a right to learn the authentic art and not a poorer imitation. Remember that Tai Chi has been developed over hundreds of years, during which time it has been synthesised and refined to become the practical tool it now is. Therefore one should take care to ensure that what is being taught has a recognised, verifiable lineage. As a guideline, the five officially recognised styles are listed here and, where applicable, styles are followed by related systems that were subsequently developed by masters.

From the time that Chang San-Feng created his original Thirteen Postures, Tai Chi has been traced back to the Wudang mountain in Hubei province and to Chenjiagou village (named after a family of the same name) in Henan province. This village is generally regarded as the birthplace of Tai Chi.

*Statue of Chang San-Feng in a temple on Wudang mountain*

## CHEN STYLE

The first recorded use of the term 'Tai Chi' was in the 17th century. Chen Wang-Ting from Chenjiagou ('Chen') village, Wenxian county, Henan province began teaching what we now refer to as Tai Chi in around 1650. The movements of Chen Style Tai Chi are often very dynamic, containing more evidently martial applications. This is in marked contrast to some of the quieter, softer techniques seen in other recognised systems. Chen Style includes both fast and slow movement, sudden foot-stomping and rapid fist movements as well as slow, twisting, spiralling movements from the waist. The briefest glance at the names of the movements, like 'Buddha Warrior Attendant Pounds the Mortar' and 'Tornado Foot', gives a sense of the intentions employed in the execution of the postures.

## CHEN STYLE TODAY

For many years, because Chenjiagou village was very small and because the early Chen family instructors never travelled too far afield, the Chen Style of Tai Chi was still a relatively closely-guarded secret. When China lifted many of the travel restrictions on her own people, Chen Tai Chi started to spread from the village to the bigger towns and cities. The new openness also led to the spread of this and many other arts from China to the rest of the world. Although this openness greatly increased the popularity of this dynamic approach to the art, Chen

Style still retains close connections with the original Chen family. Two of its biggest and best-known proponents are Chen Zhen Lei and Chen Xiao Wang. Chen Zhen Lei still lives in the village and Chen Xiao Wang resides in Australia. They are both still very active on the Tai Chi circuit, regularly teaching in Asia, Europe and America. The Chen Style is also one of the four styles included in the competition routines of the Chinese Wushu Association. Today Chen village has become something of a tourist attraction, with an increasing number of tours being organised to bring Tai Chi students from all parts of the world to undergo short training courses with eminent masters from the family. There is also a major annual exhibition and tournament.

## YANG STYLE

Yang Lu Chan (1799–1872) is reported to have moved to the Chen village to learn the art of Tai Chi from the Chen family. As he was not a member of their family, they refused to teach him their system of Chinese boxing or Tai Chi. Legend has it that Yang worked in the Chen village and when the Chen family were training in their martial skills he secretly observed them. He diligently practised each of their fighting routines and techniques, reaching a very high level of proficiency. One day when all the men of Chenjiagou village were out of the area, people arrived from out of town to steal from them. Yang Lu Chan, who remained behind, fought and saw off these invaders, using the skills he had worked hard to attain. When the men of the village returned they heard what he had done and, understanding his serious approach to learning Tai Chi, decided to teach him. He then went on to develop his own style of Tai Chi.

After some time Yang Lu Chan moved to Beijing and taught the Imperial Guard Tai Chi. In moving from a small village to the major city he was instrumental in spreading Tai Chi throughout the country. He also adapted many aspects of the Chen Style, removing the stomps and rapid punches to make it more accessible. The Yang Style has more open, expansive movements and is probably the most popular style practised today.

## YANG STYLE TODAY

Yang Lu Chan taught his son, Yang Jianhou (1839–1917), who in turn taught his son Yang Chengfu (1883–1936). Those individuals and other members of their family are largely responsible for the spread of Tai Chi throughout China, Asia and the Western world. By amending some of the postures, and promoting the health aspects, they took the art to the common man and ultimately made it an everyday part of Chinese life. Yang Style Tai Chi and its offshoots are probably more practised than any other style. Currently, two descended members of the Yang family are extensively travelling and teaching this most popular style: Yang Zhen Duo and his nephew, Yang Jun. It is also one of the four routines approved by the Chinese Wushu Association for competitions.

## WU STYLE

Wu Style Tai Chi was developed by Wu Yu-Hsing (1812–80). Wu Yu-Hsing was supposedly on his way to learn Chen Style Tai Chi when he and his two brothers heard about Yang Lu Chan. He learned

Yang Style Tai Chi from Yang Lu Chan but also spent some time working with Chen Jing Ping. The style he created included aspects of both the Chen and Yang styles, along with Wu's own modifications. The Wu Style is characterised by more compact, tighter movements. Where Yang Style emphasises an upright, erect spine, Wu Style maintains a sense of alignment from the coccyx (base of the spine) to the crown of the head that also allows the body to incline forwards or backwards.

Wu Yu-Hsing's son, Wu Chien Chuan, learned from his father and went on to be employed as teacher to the Imperial Guard. Wu Chien Chuan's daughter Wu Ying Hua also studied Tai Chi with her father, as did her husband Mah Yeuh Liang, who went on to become a renowned figure in Tai Chi circles. They lived and taught in Shanghai, both remaining active participants in the Tai Chi community until they died in the late 1990s aged 94 and 97 respectively. Wu Style Tai Chi was predominantly taught and practised in southern China and Hong Kong as many of the family members lived or taught there.

## WU STYLE TODAY

There are a number of Wu family members living and teaching in Canada, with branches in the UK. The son of Wu Ying Hua and Mah Yeuh Liang, Ma Jing Bao, continues the family tradition in the Netherlands and Germany, where he lives and works.

## SUN STYLE

Sun Style Tai Chi was created by Sun Lutang (1861–1933). He originally learned Wu Style and integrated it with his knowledge of other Chinese internal arts like Hsing-I and Pa Kua. Although largely unknown outside China, it is one of the four main styles accepted and approved for competition. Movements in the Sun Style are short and compact with upright postures.

## SUN STYLE TODAY

Sun Lutang's daughter Sun Jian Yun is considered to be a Grandmaster of Sun Style Taijiquan ('Taijiquan' is another translation of 'Tai Chi Chuan') and is one of the few women to hold this illustrious title. When the Chinese Wushu Association formed the standardised routines for competition she strongly objected to the changes they applied to her father's system and tried to maintain its authenticity. The changes went through and her name was removed from the verifying committee of the competition styles. There are a few practitioners of Sun Style around and as Tai Chi continues to spread it is probably ensured a permanent place in the recognised routines.

## CHENG MAN-CHING

Cheng Man-ching was an artist, calligrapher and poet when he moved to Shanghai to become director of the painting department at the Shanghai School of Fine Arts. He had been suffering from tuberculosis when in 1932 he was introduced to Yang Chengfu and began his training in Tai Chi. Professor Cheng went on to Taiwan where he taught Tai Chi to the soldiers of Chiang Kai-Shek. The original Yang Style Tai Chi form consisted of 108 movements that took a long time to learn. This was impractical in a military context. Cheng shortened the system to two groups of 44 and 37 movements to allow the army to learn the routines in a shorter time. He retained all of the essential elements of the system and dispensed with many of the repetitions that were originally included.

In the mid-1960s Professor Cheng moved to America and opened a school for Tai Chi in New York. He was the first Chinese master who openly taught the art to non-Chinese. His shortened system allowed them to learn the movements within a reasonable time span. As he had adapted the original Yang Style and had been responsible for introducing the knowledge of the art to the Western world, his system is now known as Cheng Man-ching Tai Chi.

## OTHER RECOGNISED STYLES

From those early styles there are a number of offshoots that are now accepted, but in order for them to be regarded as Tai Chi they should be able to show a clear lineage from the original recognised systems. They must also adhere to the principles of the art.

# What makes Tai Chi unique?

In Western culture the general idea behind exercise is to do something vigorous that increases the heart rate and leaves the exerciser feeling like they have 'worked out'. In contrast, during the practice of Tai Chi the movements are slow and even and the breathing relaxed and natural. The breathing should remain deep and slow rather than short and quick. In coordinating movements with breathing and focus of the mind, the flow of internal energy is stimulated through meridians or pathways in the body that, in turn, help to promote the body's natural healing energy. Through the slow, gradual process of transferring weight from one leg to the other, strength is developed in the legs, and the body is allowed to become aware of each aspect of the art, each nuance of moving from one foot to the other. The centre of gravity moves from the upper body and chest down to the lower abdomen. This helps to release the stress and tension that often accumulate in the head, neck, shoulders and back by letting it 'ground' into the earth. The upper body becomes light and flexible, with a feeling of being suspended from above. This allows the joints to open and release, which in turn helps to prevent the development of blockages and tension.

By moving through each transition slowly and evenly, the body is being gently trained to identify its most effectively ergonomic way of moving. When the practitioner moves, the focus should be on moving from the waist rather than from the upper body. This prevents extraneous motion, ultimately leading to an increase in mechanical effectiveness.

When movements are coupled with slow, natural breathing a smooth, even pace can be found that helps to induce relaxation and reduce stress. With over-excitement come movements that are uncoordinated and ineffective, often causing negative effects, which in extreme circumstances can badly affect spatial awareness. Through continuous practice of the Tai Chi forms the practitioner will come to know his or her body well, making it more efficient.

Imagine dropping a ream of paper so that 500 sheets are scattered on the ground. They could be picked up by the handful and shuffled together. Consider how they would look after placing them in a pile on a desk. Not too orderly perhaps? Now think about picking up the paper sheet by sheet and carefully placing each sheet one on top of the other, taking care to see that each corner matches with the sheet below. After some time the result would be a much neater pile of paper.

*The tortoise is a symbol of longevity*

In Tai Chi, through the slow execution of each posture, discovering how each position feels in the body, working through each interconnecting movement, the practitioner will after some time become familiar with the workings of his or her body. This is not to say that everybody needs to aspire to perfectly aligned forms, with everything precisely where it ought to be, but becoming aware of one's body is worthwhile in its own right.

Think about the old tale of the hare and the tortoise. The hare spends his time frantically rushing from place to place while the old tortoise crawls at a leisurely speed. Who will live the longest? People are all given much the same resources when they are born and if they are expended quickly, they will soon be gone. Tai Chi helps individuals to conserve their internal energy and ultimately, with regular practice, this will lead to a long and happy life.

# Principles of Tai Chi

## Postures

When Chang San-Feng visualised the fight between the bird and the snake it was not enough to imagine that those movements could be immediately adapted and applied in a defensive or offensive manner. In creating the original Thirteen Postures, which laid the foundation for what eventually became Tai Chi, Chang San-Feng also brought to bear his knowledge of Taoist belief, yin/yang philosophy, traditional Chinese medicine and astrology.

The Thirteen Postures were devised by combining the Eight Powers with the Five Elements.

### THE EIGHT POWERS

In looking more closely at the development of the philosophy of Tai Chi, the *I Ching* or *Book of Changes* needs to be considered. The *I Ching* involves a series of lines in a system of symbolism which illustrates the different states of flux which are so important to Eastern thought. These interpretations are made possible by looking at the interplay of energies as represented through permutations of solid —— (yang) or broken – – (yin) lines.

The different combinations of three of these lines create the trigrams. These trigrams represent the four cardinal directions of north, south, east and west and their respective diagonal directions, northeast,

*The Eight Powers are behind the main movements in Tai Chi*

northwest, southeast and southwest. During the practice of Tai Chi each direction is covered, creating protection from all sides. The trigrams also relate to the powers used in the martial application of Tai Chi.

The powers are are Peng, Lu, Chi, An, Cai, Li, Zhou and Cao.

| The Eight Powers relate to the trigrams as follows: | |
| --- | --- |
| Chien = Peng | Sun = Cai |
| Kun = Lu | Chen = Lieh |
| Kan = Chi | Tui = Zhou |
| Li = An | Ken = Cao |

Whatever a person's reason for practising Tai Chi, having an awareness of the purpose of each movement improves performance and increases the benefits in all other areas – health, relaxation and energy development.

These Eight Powers are right at the heart of the several movements that deal, in different ways, with defending against attacks.

## 1. PENG

*Peng* is the energy that is used in the Ward Off posture.

In the Peng action the arms rise upwards and create a 'bouncing' or uplifting energy to repel an attack.

## 2. LU

*Lu* is the energy that is applied in the Roll Back posture.

In the Lu action the practitioner moves back and turns, drawing the opponent's oncoming force or energy inwards, where it becomes dissipated.

## 3. CHI

*Chi* is the energy that is applied in the Press posture.

In the Chi action the palm is pressed against the inside of the opposite wrist while penetrating this energy into the opponent. There is a sense of both penetrating and pressing either down or up.

## 4. AN

*An* is the energy that is applied in the Push posture.

In the An action the practitioner pushes into a partner's body as the former transfers weight forwards using their connection from the back foot to propel their force forward, rather than merely using the force of the arms and upper body.

## 5. CAI

*Cai* is the energy that is applied in the Pull Down.

In the Cai action the opponent's oncoming force is pulled down and allowed to be neutralised before it reaches its destination.

## 6. LI

*Li* is the energy that is applied in the Split.

In the Li action the idea is to get inside the opponent's oncoming force to open him up and dissipate his strike.

## 7. ZHOU

*Zhou* is the energy that is applied in the Elbow posture.

In the Zhou action the idea is to go inside the opponent's oncoming force to strike with your elbow.

## 8. CAO

*Cao* is the energy that is applied in the Shoulder Strike posture.

In the Cao action the practitioner goes inside the opponent's oncoming force to strike with the shoulder as the weight is transferred into him.

# The Five Elements

The notion of the Five Elements is embedded in many aspects of Chinese philosophy and culture. In traditional Chinese medicine the Five Elements are used to represent the qualities of the internal organs: the heart, lungs, liver, spleen and kidney relate to Fire, Metal, Wood, Earth and Water respectively. The Five Elements relate to Tai Chi through the ways of stepping in and evading attacks. Each element relates to a particular direction.

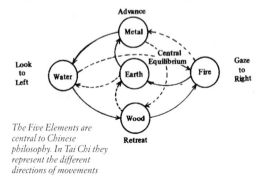

*The Five Elements are central to Chinese philosophy. In Tai Chi they represent the different directions of movements*

This is how the Five Elements relate to the different directions in which the Tai Chi practitioner might move while performing the art:

| | |
|---|---|
| Metal | Forward |
| Fire | Right |
| Wood | Back |
| Water | Left |
| Earth | Centre |

In dealing with the tactics employed, the relationship of each element to each of the other ones should be considered.

- In the Creative Cycle the Five Elements produce each other:
  Wood creates Fire, Fire creates Earth, Earth creates Metal, Metal creates Water and Water creates Wood.

- In the Destructive Cycle the Five Elements can destroy each other:
Metal destroys Wood, Wood destroys Earth, Earth destroys Water, Water destroys Fire and Fire destroys Metal.

The movements have been constructed relative to the different elements and how they affect each other, both creatively and destructively.

- If an attack comes from the front (Metal) direction one may move back to avoid it (Wood) as Metal can destroy Wood.

- If an attack comes from the left (Water), moving to the right (Fire) could provide a suitable defence as Water can destroy Fire.

# TAI CHI PRACTICE

The most commonly known aspect of Tai Chi is the Hand Form but variations of the exercises are also performed with weapons. There are Straight Sword, Sabre and Spear forms and also the less familiar Tai Chi Ruler and Fan forms. Regular practice of these sequences will help to increase energy levels and encourage calmness and focus. Continuous practice will also help to correct postural defects, raise confidence and let the practitioner relate more effectively to others.

Starting on page 109 is a series of postures from the first section of the Short Yang Form that will take only three minutes to complete. They will provide a taste of what Tai Chi can offer. Study each posture carefully and the advice given on transitions and purpose. Once learned, the routine can be practised three or four times a session and benefits can be gained that are close to those that would be achieved through performing an entire form of Tai Chi.

- In learning the movements it is recommended that practitioners start with one or two postures, familiarising themselves with them through regular practice, and then gradually, piece by piece, adding the next postures until they have the complete Hand Form.

- A typical Hand Form can take from 9 to 25 minutes to perform. As a rough guideline it will take approximately one year to learn a Hand Form. With committed, regular practice, this time span can be shortened. However, the practitioner should not let the time factor dissuade him or her, as after only a few sessions he or she will start to feel the benefits.

- When learning any discipline the aim is obviously to become familiar with that which is being taught. With a Tai Chi form containing a limited number of movements people often place the emphasis on learning the complete sequence as quickly as possible. Try to be patient and don't lose sight of the fact that the benefits of Tai Chi come gradually through regular practice.

- Whether the practice is of a few movements over the space of a 30-minute session or one complete Hand Form, it doesn't really matter. By going through each transition, over and over again, the rewards are reaped in the same way.

- With Tai Chi it is better just to do each movement or transition and not be in too much of a hurry to reach the end of the sequence of movements. By practising in this way it will be possible to integrate each aspect of the system more fully.

- The more the practitioner practises, the more familiar he or she will become with the quality of movement, and benefit.

# The postures or movements

The sequence of movements in Tai Chi consists of a series of postures that are linked together by slowly transferring between one movement and the next.

Many of the postures in Tai Chi include characteristics of different animals. In Chinese culture the language is often poetic and includes colourful, evocative imagery. The names of the postures often help to identify the nature or the quality of movement.

---

### SOME POSTURE NAMES

- White Crane Spreads Wings
- Embrace Tiger, Return to Mountain
- Snake Creeps Down
- Golden Rooster Stands on One Leg

---

When performing these postures one should bear in mind the movement qualities of the respective creatures. A white crane spreading his wings (*see stage 33 of* **The Short Yang Form**, *page 141*) conjures up the image of a large bird on one leg with its wings opening up and outwards. In Tai Chi the practitioner would be positioned on his or her right leg with the left toe merely making contact with the ground in front. The right arm is held up in front of the head, opening up the upper chest, and the left hand is placed as a counterbalance down beside the hips. This imagery helps the practitioner to understand exactly how the postures should be performed.

When these postures are being performed they are gently opening up areas of the body to increase the flow of internal energy through the meridians or pathways. In lifting the arms, the meridians that run along the inside of the arms are being opened up, and by holding leg postures or slowly transferring from one to the other the flow of energy along the meridians that run inside the legs is being promoted. In slowly moving the body through each connecting posture at a regular, even pace the free flow of energy through all of the main meridians in the body is guaranteed.

It should also be mentioned that in certain forms of Chi Kung or energy-promoting exercises (Zhan Zhong), static postures can be held that are similar to those in Tai Chi, and the internal energy will find its own way through the meridians.

# The Ten Essentials

In Tai Chi, like any other art, there are a number of basic principles that should be adhered to when practising. These are a series of rules that are applied to recognised styles of Tai Chi. In this book the focus is on the Yang Style but the principles can be applied to any recognised style. Central to the Yang Style are the criteria of the Ten Essentials as written by Yang Chengfu.

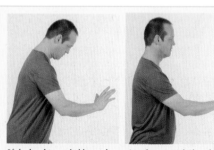

*If the head is not held upright, the flow of energy will be interrupted*

*Aim for a straight line from base of spine to crown of head*

## 1. KEEP THE HEAD ERECT

Imagine that your head is being suspended from above. With the head suspended, the body creates a straight line for the spirit to rise from the base of the spine to the crown of the head.

## 2. HOLLOW THE CHEST

A chest 'hollowed' or relaxed will help to release tension from the upper body and allow the *chi* energy to settle in the lower dantien, the area just around the navel.

*The upper body and limbs should not be tense*

*The chest should feel 'hollowed' and relaxed*

## 3. RELAX THE WAIST

Relaxation and movement from the waist encourage a more efficient use of the body. Situations of conflict tend to make people tighten up and hold energy in their upper bodies and chests. By relaxing the waist they can release tension from this area, and thus enhance their performance.

## 4. DIFFERENTIATE BETWEEN SUBSTANTIAL AND INSUBSTANTIAL

It is important to recognise the points at which the weight of the body is transferring from one foot to the other. In the majority of stances weight is distributed 70 per cent on one leg, 30 per cent on the other.

## 5. SINK THE SHOULDERS AND ELBOWS

By sinking the shoulders and elbows a free flow of energy is established from the soles of the feet, through the spine, along the arms and into the hands. Raising the shoulders and elbows creates blockages which can impede the natural energy flow through the body.

*A common mistake is to lift the shoulders and elbows*

*The impression should be one of 'sinking' the shoulders and elbows*

## 6. APPLY YI RATHER THAN MUSCULAR FORCE

When executing movements the mind (*yi*) should be applied rather than muscular force. Using the mind to visualise the application of the movement increases a person's effectiveness beyond mere physical strength.

## 7. COORDINATE THE UPPER AND LOWER BODY

When the body moves, it moves as one unit with a connection between the upper and lower torso.

The movements originate from the waist as the central axis and everything else follows as one connected unit.

## 8. COORDINATE THE INNER AND OUTER PARTS

Every movement comes from the connection between the mind and the body: when the mind dictates the direction the body should move with it. By harmonising the inner and outer shape of the forms results can be achieved. Tai Chi relaxes both mind and body, while strengthening muscles and enhancing wellbeing.

## 9. CONTINUOUS AND FLOWING MOVEMENTS

When performing the form, moves should be smooth and even, and carried out in a continuous, flowing manner. An expression applied to Tai Chi is 'Move like pulling silk from a cocoon.' In Chen Style Tai Chi a routine is practised called Reeling Silk which involves moving in a smooth, regular fashion from the waist.

## 10. INNER TRANQUILLITY AND PEACE IN MOVEMENT

'Move like a river, be as still as a mountain.' This is an expression that illustrates the quality of movement that should be applied to the performance of the postures. The mind is still and relaxed while the body moves at an even, regular pace. By practising in this way, a harmonious connection between the mind and body can be achieved.

# What physical condition is required?

Tai Chi is truly accessible to people of all ages and most physical conditions. Today there is a wide range of classes catering for everyone from young, physically active students to senior citizens, and to those with some physical impairment.

Tai Chi requires little physical effort as it works by developing internal energy in the body rather than by hard physical exertion. Each movement is performed slowly, at the student's own even pace. There are no strong stretches and there is no pressure for the individual to extend beyond his or her physical ability. If the student is approaching exercise after some years of absence, or recovering from a debilitating illness or other health problem, or if they are overweight, Tai Chi provides a way of reintroducing the body to slow, gentle exercise. The overriding principle is one of slow, gradual development that allows the body to find its own level gently and, through regular practice, safely increase its capabilities.

Those who are in peak physical condition gained through vigorous training schedules may also find that Tai Chi allows more effective movement, increases focus and body awareness and ultimately improves performance levels.

Today there are also a number of instructors who have adapted Tai Chi for those with special needs. From people who may be in wheelchairs or are recovering from movement-affecting conditions like strokes, or for those with vision difficulties, Tai Chi offers a safe, accessible method of exercise. When the body or mind has suffered a form of trauma that has an effect on its range of movement it is important to find a way to gently retrain the parts that have been harmed. Tai Chi is the ideal vehicle for reacquainting the body and mind with the mechanisms by which they operate. Slow, regular repetition of the sequences will greatly aid this process. Not only will the individual gain from the physical benefits, but by working in conjunction with the breath, will also achieve a relaxed mind and, ultimately, raised spirits.

# Benefits

The practice of Tai Chi provides benefits on many levels, some of which will be felt within a few sessions while others will develop as part of a more long-term process. Aside from the evident physical benefits, Tai Chi will ultimately show positive consequences in other areas of the practitioner's life. Not only does it increase awareness of the structure of the body and how it is used, but it also affects thought and relationships with others. This altered perspective will improve many aspects of the practitioner's physical and mental health and general wellbeing.

## MENTAL BENEFITS

- Improved focus and clarity of thought
- A calm, relaxed mind
- More patience and understanding
- Less susceptible to stress
- Balanced approach to conflict

## PHYSICAL BENEFITS

- Improved immune system
- Greater flexibility
- Postural awareness
- More effective use of the body
- Better balance
- Increased energy
- Fewer stress-induced pains

# How are these benefits achieved?

The simplest way to achieve the benefits offered by Tai Chi is through regular practice. It's as easy as that. The more you do it, the easier it becomes and the more benefits are gained. There is no need to practice secret, esoteric routines and no need to work under the tutelage of an enlightened master. The benefits of Tai Chi really are there for all to achieve. The objective should be to learn a few simple movements and carefully consider how they are shaped and formed and how they feel in the body. With regular application, and by looking at the principles and techniques in relation to everyday life, students will gain an increased understanding both of themselves and of others.

## COMMITMENT

There is a famous story of an old Tai Chi master who was working in his field planting rice. He was well

versed in all the martial applications of the art and for
many, many years he remained the undefeated
champion. This caused great consternation to a
certain young master who wanted to achieve the fame
of becoming the best. As the old master was planting
his crop the young man crept up behind him in
preparation for the attack. When he felt his time was
right the young man jumped forward to strike the old
man. Just at that moment the old man turned and
parried the attack, throwing his assailant to the
ground. 'How can you do that?' shouted the young
man. 'For seven hours every day I've diligently
practised in order to be able to defeat you. How is this
possible? How many hours do you spend practising
each day?' With a smile the old man answered, '24
hours a day.' And then he returned to his business of
planting the crops for the next season's harvest.

What is meant by this tale is that the principles of Tai
Chi remained with the old master through his daily
life. It was something much more than a pursuit he
practised for a few hours a day or week. If a person
allows the principles of Tai Chi to be a part of every

aspect of life, including his or her social and working life, he or she will find that the benefits help him or her to become a more centred, focused, and well-rounded individual.

# Points to consider when practising

Tai Chi is a movement exercise that helps to improve posture. By paying attention to certain aspects of posture, performance will be assisted. The practitioner should ensure that these few points are at the forefront of his or her mind throughout their regular practice.

## ALIGNMENT

In maintaining correct alignment in the body, a clear pathway for the internal energy to move through the meridians is being created. The easier its route the better it will flow. Notice if the head is being dropped forward or back or the back is bowing. Even when

the body is bent forward, a straight line from the base
of the spine to the crown of the head should be
maintained.

*It is important to keep a straight line running through the whole body (right) rather than dropping the head and shoulders forwards or back (left)*

## RELAXED LIMBS

By keeping the arms and legs soft and open, rather
than holding them tight or rigid, the free flow of
energy through the body will be assisted. Consider a

twisted garden hose that has a kink in it. This will inhibit the free flow of water and prevent the hose from doing its job. When the hose has no stress or tension along its length everything is able to move freely. Think of this openness in the limbs while moving through the postures.

## HAND POSITION

The hands should be relaxed and open with no tension, but they should not be so relaxed that they feel limp or insipid. If the palms are held as though being warmed over an open fire, this should allow the energy to be felt through them. Try to concentrate awareness on the 'Laogong point' at the centre of the palms.

*Keep the hands relaxed and open, to allow the free flow of energy*

## CONNECTING TO THE GROUND

Always take sufficient time to establish a connection with the ground when moving from one posture to the next. Consider the fact that the weight of the body does not merely end on the surface of the floor. When the weight is being transferred from one foot to the other, ensure that the leg is not straightened or locked. If either leg is locked, balancing becomes more difficult. Get a sense of letting the weight fall from one foot into the ground before lifting the other foot. When a step forwards or backwards is made, maintain a low centre of gravity in the body.

## OVEREXTENDING

Try to maintain a good sense of balance between the aspects of yin and yang when performing the movements. Pushing forwards should not involve locking the arms, and when the weight shifts back or forwards the limbs should not be locked.

*Limbs should remain supple and flexible at all times*

*Do not exaggerate movements. This leads to the locking of limbs*

## MENTAL IMAGERY

As previously mentioned, the application of the mind plays a critical part in the practice of Tai Chi. By maintaining a focus of intent towards the purpose of the movements, performance is greatly enhanced.

## ROOTING

Visualisation is an important tool in Tai Chi. Before they begin carrying out any postures, some Tai Chi practitioners find it useful to try and imagine that the soles of their feet have roots growing from them. Letting those roots plant themselves deep into the earth is an effective way of establishing a firm connection with the ground. Many people say that you should learn Tai Chi from the ground upwards. By establishing a connection with the ground a firm base from which to develop is created.

## CONCENTRATE ON YOUR LOWER DANTIEN

The lower dantien is an area found in the torso, just around the navel. In Tai Chi, this is where the energy is stored. Let the breathing relax into the lower abdomen and focus on this area. Imagine the area becoming warmer as the energy is stored in preparation for movement through the form.

## FEELING THE AIR

When performing the movements, try to notice the air as the limbs move through it. Let the soft breeze that comes from the movement be felt on the back of the hands and fingers. This will encourage a relaxed feeling rather than having tightness in the arms or fingers.

## 'SETTING THE SCENE'

In preparation, take a moment or two to think about the energy travelling through the body, from the soles of the feet to the crown of the head.

---

### STRESS RELIEF

Keeping both the body and mind relaxed and open, and coupling this with correct posture, will assist the free flow of energy. A relaxed mind and deep, abdominal breathing help to lower demands on the body and mind and reduce the likelihood of stress.

# A useful preparation exercise

Although performing Tai Chi is very calming and relaxing, practice can be enhanced greatly if a few minutes are taken to prepare the mind and focus the energy beforehand.

The practitioner should imagine that he or she is a small child about to take its first steps. A child will go through several stages, and so should the practitioner. Gradually the child stands up and finds an upright position. Then it tries to find its balance and let the weight go onto one leg. This is the point where many can fail.

Balance is an integral part of what is being taught in a Tai Chi class. Often a Tai Chi session begins by establishing an awareness of how the weight is distributed between the feet. Everything in Tai Chi begins by establishing a firm connection with the ground. It is the most important aspect.

- Stand up. Concentrate on exactly how it feels to be standing upright. This is not something that human beings consider that often. It is taken for granted. Now pay attention to the body's connection with the ground. What part of the feet is the contact through? Is it more at the front of the foot, the sides or the back? If you become aware that too much weight is being placed on any part of the foot try to correct this. There is a point at the middle of the front of the sole that is called the Yongquan Point or 'Bubbling Spring'. According to Tai Chi theory, it is from here that the energy is drawn from the earth. At the top of the head is the Beihui Point where, the theory goes, the connection with the heavens is achieved. Think about this connection moving through the body, from the soles of the feet to the crown of the head.

- Relax the knee joints. If the legs are locked it is harder to balance. Creating softness in the knees also eases a person's impact on the ground. Think about the hips. Are they relaxed and down or does the pelvis protrude forward or back? Imagine having a large, heavy tail and that the weight of that tail pulls down on the lower hips, slightly tucking them inwards. This should create a situation where the back is better aligned.

- Imagine that your head is suspended from above with a thread at the back of the top of it, allowing your body to be correctly aligned. The chin should be relaxed and the shoulders should be allowed to drop a little more. Soften the elbows and open the palms. Begin to place the focus on the centre of the palms (Laogong Point).

- Spend a couple of minutes in the stance, letting the breath deepen to the lower abdomen. This connection, from the soles of the feet, through the ankles, up the inside of the legs and connecting at the base of the spine, up the spine, through the neck and up to the crown of the head should be borne in mind throughout. The path should be open and the body relaxed. Think of letting everything from below the waist drop to the ground, and everything above the waist being open and light, connecting to the heavens.

- This is the first position in Tai Chi. It is also the most important position. Before the journey can be started, there must be preparation. Taking time to pay attention to the body, to relax the mind and breath and to establish connections above and below the body allows harmony within the individual and, in turn, with the external world. Even if nothing else is firmly established in a Tai Chi class a lot can be gained from mastering this one simple exercise.

Today, people rarely take the time to stop and pay attention to themselves, where they are in their bodies, their minds and their inner beings. If they could learn to take a little time to slow down and enjoy the miracle of standing, this would be of great benefit to them. A feeling of connection with the earth and the heavens recharges inner batteries, rejuvenates and replenishes lost energy.

# What happens in a typical class?

Because of its many-layered nature there are a great variety of things that can be taught in a Tai Chi class. However, the common thread, whatever the style or approach, is the Hand Form. This is the base upon which everything else in the discipline is built.

## LOOSENING EXERCISES

One of the first things that may be taught is a series of loosening-up exercises. These are designed to relax

*Loosening up is an important preliminary exercise*

the body in order to allow the energy to flow through the meridians. They generally focus on turning from the waist while relaxing the arms and shoulders. As the movements in Tai Chi centre on moving from the waist rather than the upper body, time spent developing this aspect will greatly assist overall development.

## BODY AWARENESS

In order to increase the individual's understanding of Tai Chi movement, some work may be done to increase overall body awareness. There are a number of ways of identifying how the body feels, all of which can be learned. One method teaches the student to bring their attention to various points throughout their body, while focusing on how connected the body and mind are with the ground below and the heavens above.

## LEARNING THE HAND FORM

The next step is to learn a few postures of the Hand Form. The student will be told how to place his or her arms, hands and body in various positions or postures. The instructor will advise on how to stand, how to hold the arms and how fast to move. It is advisable for the beginner to learn one or two movements and practise them on their own many times. The more regular the practice, the easier it will be both to understand and to remember the sequence of movements. Try to be patient and allow the body time to get accustomed to the nature of the movements. Remember that people spend most of their time moving fairly quickly without thinking about it. It is unusual for them to slow down and pay attention to how their bodies work. It is important to relax the mind as well as the body when practising.

Gradually, little by little, the component parts of the Hand Form will become familiar and the student will be able to enjoy the practice without constantly trying to remember how the movements are linked to each other.

Also, students should not put pressure on themselves to learn a specific set of movements over a specific time span. People all learn at different paces and there

*Regular practice will ensure that movements are retained*

will always be a wide range of abilities in the class. Since Tai Chi aims to establish sequences through the body mind rather than the cerebral mind, intellectual reasoning is not being applied to the learning process. Never be in a hurry to learn. By learning slowly, over a sustained practice period, movements will be retained well.

## CONTINUITY

Initially, when practising the transitions from one posture to the next, they may seem stilted and uncoordinated. Through regular practice, a smooth transition from one posture to another will be achieved, and the observer will not be able to see the joins or connecting movements. Although individual sequences are taught, with an emphasis on stance and posture, the ultimate aim is to give the performance a smooth continuous rhythm. Remember the saying, 'Move like a river, be as still as a mountain.' This means that inside the body and mind there should be a sense of stillness or calmness, while on the outside the movements should be even and regular. There should be no sudden movements, speeding up or slowing down. The visual appeal of Tai Chi comes from its smooth, natural pace with everything being just where it ought to be.

## MEDITATION

Instructors may include some meditation exercises in their class. It is often said that Tai Chi is a movement meditation in itself, inducing calm meditative feelings during practice. However, some instructors may include static meditation to help calm the mind either before or immediately after performing the routine of the Hand Form.

# Chi Kung

Chi Kung is a term applied to myriad exercises designed to promote the flow of energy through the meridians of the body. There are many varied approaches to Chi Kung; some are simple static forms, done either sitting or standing, while others are more elaborate.

Some of the most popular styles practised in Tai Chi classes are:

Eight Brocade

Tai Chi Chi Kung

Zhan Zhuang

With the exception of static Chi Kung exercises, during which the practitioner either sits or stands and visualises the energy moving through the body, Chi Kung is practised by combining a series of movements with the breathing and focus of the mind.

Three basic components are generally incorporated in the practice of Chi Kung exercises:

1. Movement
2. Breathing
3. *Yi* or focus of the mind

Essentially, Chi Kung is a system of energy-promoting exercises that are designed to improve health.

Tai Chi Chi Kung was developed by isolating a few postures from the Tai Chi Hand Form and creating movements that are easier to learn, but still maintain many of the benefits of Tai Chi.

Starting on the opposite page is a series of photographs illustrating a simple but highly effective Tai Chi Chi Kung exercise for students to try:

# FLYING WILD GOOSE

Stand with the feet shoulder-distance apart, the shoulders relaxed and hands open, focusing on the centres of the palms. Relax the breathing.

2

Keeping the shoulders relaxed, start slowly to lift the arms out from the body in time with an in-breath, still focusing on the centres of the palms.

Still breathing in, raise the arms until they become parallel with the ground. Continue to feel the connection through the palms.

Start gently to bend the knees, sinking down, as the out-breath is started, and let the arms slowly drop down at the same time.

Allow the arms to rest back down by the sides as the knees are gradually bent. Keep focusing on the palms and moving in with the breath.

# Nei Kung

Nei Kung is an internal exercise system used both to increase the body's internal strength and to help protect it against attacks. Some practitioners regard Nei Kung as an essential ingredient when using Tai Chi for martial purposes. Certain exercises are performed in conjunction with the breath and together these toughen the martial artist's body against blows.

One of the highlights of many martial arts tournaments involves an impressive display of apparently supernatural powers where performers might have slabs smashed against their head or body with a heavy hammer. To withstand these blows, extensive Nei Kung training has usually been undergone. Often this training is started at a very young age. Nei Kung is a part of the Tai Chi practice of only a few people. However, it is almost invariably practised by those at a very advanced level.

# Partner work

While the Hand Form is a very special solo exercise which can be practised by the individual or in groups, it is also advisable to do some partner work. Partner exercises develop sensitivity, and are a valuable if not essential part of learning Tai Chi. A person's Hand Form may become beautiful to watch but in order to really understand how effective it is partner work is invaluable.

## STICKING HANDS

Some simple partner exercises may be done to help develop an awareness of how strong the posture is and how relaxed the individual is in situations of conflict. A common exercise to start with is Sticking Hands. This involves resting one hand on a partner's wrist and closing the eyes. The pupil will then be led around the room, moving in different directions, up and down, forward and back, or from left to right. The arm should act as an antenna with which the individual can 'listen' through the fingers to where the partner is leading them. The more the person being led can stay relaxed, in body and mind, the easier it will be for the individual to sense where the partner is leading them. Start off working slowly, taking great care to become aware of the partner's limitations. By working gently and with consideration, both practitioners' capabilities will be extended. Alternate roles, so that each partner gets to lead and be led.

*For the Sticking Hands exercise one partner (left) closes their eyes and rests a hand on the wrist of the 'leader' (right)*

*The partner is then moved in different directions, from left to right or up and down*

*With time the individual begins to sense which direction their partner is about to lead them in*

## YIELDING EXERCISES

In the principles of Tai Chi the theory goes that when extreme yang is reached it becomes yin. When people sense an attack, whether physical or psychological and emotional, they often tense up in defence. This creates a weakness, and in the long term is ineffectual. Through working *with* a physical force or attack, not only can increased confidence be achieved but also a relaxed, more creative response.

One partner stands, with their eyes either open or closed, while the second gently pushes them on the front of each shoulder, each side of the pelvis and then on the back of each shoulder, pushing them forwards and downwards. This exercise starts very slowly to allow the person being pushed to respond relative to the degree of the push. It is important that they have the opportunity to really 'feel' the push. Gradually, as their ability to move in relationship to the push increases, the pushes become stronger and quicker. Working this way helps to increase flexibility and retrain the body to yield to force rather than push against it.

*Push Hands relies on the idea of neutralising energy rather than opposing it. The individual on the left pushes the wrist of the person on the right. When the partner responds to the push she in turn softens her wrist*

## TUI SHOU OR PUSH HANDS

Once the concept of yielding to an oncoming force is familiar, ability is developed further through the art of Tui Shou or Push Hands.

At the early stages of learning Push Hands, a carefully structured form must be learned. There are many variations on this exercise, depending on the style of Tai Chi being practised, but they all adhere to the same principles. The first step is to have one partner pushing, with his or her palm against the wrist of the other. When the partner pushes back against the palm of the hand, the wrist is softened in response, the elbow dropped, and the waist turned. This allows the practitioner to absorb the partner's energy and force, and neutralise it into the ground. When the partner's yang force has been fully expended or neutralised, the practitioner then turns his or her hands and returns that energy by pushing back. If, however, the practitioner were to push too far, or overextend, he or she would then pull the partner downwards, behind him or her.

In the Tai Chi postures either one or both arms are often in front of the body. This is where defence is created. If the arms were held tightly either close to or around the front of the body, it would merely provide a solid surface for the partner to push against. Imagine pushing against a solid door. It's easy, the more solid a surface is, the easier it is to push against. Now imagine pushing through a curtain. It will move aside but it will also stay hanging from its rail.

In not holding the arms near or around the body, enough space is allowed to move with the partner's push, instead of allowing them to push against the body, where they could connect through to their opponent's point of balance. As the partner pushes against their opponent's soft, pliable arms, the latter should be able to discern where in their body they are pushing from, what direction it is taking the body in, and how to overcome that force to avoid being pushed over.

## FREE PUSHING

When the basic Push Hands exercises have been developed, the student can then proceed to Free Pushing. This exercise trains the individual to incorporate the principles that have been developed in a structured routine against free-form pushes. In Free Pushing one should try to 'listen' to the opponent's energy or intention in order to allow an appropriate reaction. During Free Pushing it is important to try to remain calm and relaxed. By doing so the individual will remain sensitive to the opponent's movements and intention. However, a sense of presence or 'being there' must be maintained. If a person were simply soft or relaxed without a sense of being there, it would be easy for the opponent to overcome them. When the opponent pushes, the individual should try to move relative to their push and gradually, with sensitivity, divert it away from their point of balance. There are a number of ways in which an individual can react to and deal with the pushes coming from an opponent, but in Tai Chi the concept of yielding or neutralising oncoming force rather than fighting against it is paramount. Ideally, minimum force should be used for maximum gain.

## SAN SHOU

San Shou is a series of partner exercises where strikes or blows are delivered to various parts of the body. One partner strikes while the other neutralises the oncoming force by meeting it with softness or yin energy. He or she then returns blows. Initially, these exercises are delivered softly and slowly, increasing in force and speed as experience develops. In some styles, San Shou is performed as a structured routine

or sequence that incorporates various aspects of
self-defence in a fixed pattern. Whatever the
interpretation, San Shou techniques can be adapted
for use in free sparring (fighting that is spontaneous –
free-form – but has a pre-ordained set of rules).

## DA LUI

Da Lui is a short, structured routine of movements
practised with a partner. The movements
incorporate techniques of the Eight Powers (*see*

*Da Lui uses the principle
of the Eight Powers as
its basis. For every form
of Tai Chi there is a
routine based on the
Eight Powers*

*page 41*) in a short form where one attacks as the other defends. Each Tai Chi style has its own routine based on the Eight Powers.

## MARTIAL APPLICATIONS

Each movement or Tai Chi posture carries defensive and offensive applications. To understand these applications we must return to the concept of yin and yang. Yin is considered to be the soft, feminine principle and yang the hard, masculine principle. A blow or strike would be considered to be yang force. When the force is coming towards you, you should greet it with yin or softness, thereby neutralising your opponent's strike. The postures in the Tai Chi Hand Form are constantly changing from the yin to yang aspect. By training slowly, the body becomes familiar with this constantly changing energy. Through training over a long period of time, working with a variety of these reactions can become an instinctive response in a combat situation.

# Weapon forms

There are three basic weapons that have traditionally been used in the practice of Tai Chi. They are the straight sword, the sabre and the spear, and each offers different benefits to the practitioner. Before anyone moves on to learning a weapon form they must show a high degree of proficiency in the Hand Form.

## THE STRAIGHT SWORD

The straight sword is often considered to be the tool of a gentleman and requires a great degree of sensitivity and precision.

*Straight Sword Form*

## THE SABRE

The sabre is a heavy, strong weapon. It is designed for chopping rather than the more subtle slicing and piercing of the sword.

*Sabre Form*

## THE SPEAR

When performing the Spear Form, attention is focused either on the tip of the weapon or at the point where it would be parrying an opponent's attack. Although it is a long weapon, one should still maintain an intention of the movements originating from the centre of the body.

# Dos and Don'ts

## DO

- Move at an even pace. It is said that when one practises the Hand Form one should move like a silkworm. When the silkworm weaves its thread it moves at an even pace. Moving too suddenly will snap the thread and moving too slowly will create a build-up of thread. The student should notice whether he or she is speeding up or slowing down during practice. Look for a continuum in the movements: it should not be apparent where one move ends and another begins.

- Finish one movement before going on to the next. This may seem to contradict the advice above, but often when Tai Chi practitioners become familiar with the sequence, bad habits creep in, and they start to slur the movements. Each posture has a definite finishing-point. Do not deliver the attack before this point has been reached, or the Tai Chi practice will be incomplete.

- Feel the weight transference. When transferring weight from one foot to the other, get a sense of feeling the transference. The individual should imagine that they are unsure whether the surface of the ground can take their weight and think about testing it as they transfer.

- Try to stay focused. Imagine driving a car. The driver constantly has his or her eyes on the road. They are not fixed on the surface but the awareness of the road is always there. When practising think about the movements and be totally involved in the execution of them. The practitioner may become momentarily distracted but the mind should be brought back to the intention of the movements.

## DON'T

- Overstretch any of the limbs. Always maintain a sense of balance between yin and yang when moving from one posture to another. Try to avoid over-reaching. When the weight is on the front leg, don't allow the back leg to become straight or locked, and vice versa.

- Rise up and down when transferring the weight from one foot to the other. Try to maintain a regular position height-wise. Often at the early stages of learning there is a tendency to bob up and down between transitions. With the exception of one or two movements, try to stay on the same horizontal level.

- Bring the body out of alignment. Sometimes when transferring from a back to a front stance the weight of the body can come over to one side. Get a sense of a pendulum attached to the coccyx always hanging in a straight line down from the middle of the body.

## 'BEING' TAI CHI

When the individual postures that connect together to make up the Hand Form are first learned, the attention will be on the shape and form of the movement. The eyes will study the form of the arms, legs, head and body as the student tries to emulate the teacher. It is almost as if inside the body there is the detached mind telling the limbs what to do. Once the postures and their transitions are familiar, the entire body should be involved. Think about the movement coming from inside and, in moving between postures, think not about moving the limbs but the entire body and being.

## GENERAL POINTS

- Bear in mind that Tai Chi is very different from that which is generally considered to be exercise in Western culture. There is no way to hurry things up.
- Try to set aside a regular time each day for practice. By practising regularly, benefits will gradually be achieved. Imagine trying to learn a new language by only using it for one hour a week. If it is used a little every day, eventually it will come to be known well.
- Some days you may not feel like practising too much. Don't let practice become a burden. Above all, enjoy the time spent practising.

# Trying Tai Chi

## The Short Yang Form

In the following pages we describe the first section of the Short Yang Form. This is something that is usually taught over a ten- or twelve-week course, providing an introduction to the system. Each movement is broken down into a series of component parts, illustrating each point of the transition from one posture to the next. Beginners should try to familiarise themselves with the descriptions before attempting the movements. Getting a mental picture of how the body is moving through these postures will help: where the weight should be, where in the body the movement is coming from, where the attention should be.

Work on the sequencing of one or two postures and, through a number of repetitions, allow the body to feel the transference of weight from one to the other. Take plenty of time to get familiar with these postures and transitions before moving to the next. With patience and perseverance, a sense of the quality of movement and feeling that comes from the practice of Tai Chi will gradually be achieved.

An imaginary opponent is referred to in describing the postures and transitions. As Tai Chi was originally developed as a martial art it will greatly enhance understanding of the postures and their purpose if you practise with an opponent in mind. Try to maintain an intention of executing each movement with purpose. In doing so, keep a relaxed and focused mind rather than a hard, fixed concentration.

## BREATHING

Before Tai Chi practise, time should be taken to relax the breath and focus the mind on the lower dantien (around the abdomen). When the sequence is being performed, breathing should be natural and deep. Once the movements become familiar, the breath and movement should come together. A few practitioners advocate synchronising the movement with the breath. If this technique is employed, the breath should always be natural and never forced.

# ① Preparation

- Stand with the feet shoulder-distance apart, toes pointing straight forward and weight evenly distributed.

- Relax the shoulders and elbows and focus on the centres of the palms.

- Get a sense of the weight of the body dropping through the soles of the feet and the head being suspended from above.

# ❷ Lift Hands

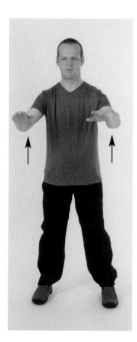

- Slowly raise the arms, keeping the shoulders, elbows and hands relaxed.
- Maintain softness in the knees and don't lock either the arms or the legs.
- Ensure that the fingers are also relaxed but not enough to become limp.

# 3 Lift Hands

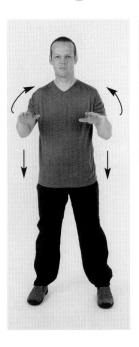

- Dropping the elbows, allow the hands to come in towards the chest.
- Keep the weight evenly distributed between both feet and ensure the body maintains an upright position.

# ④ Lower Arms

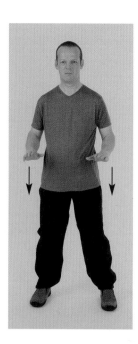

- Slowly lower the arms until they are level with the waist.

- Again keep the weight evenly balanced between both feet and maintain a straight line between the base of the spine and the crown of the head.

# 5 Sink

- As the arms come level with the waist, slowly bend the knees.

- Get a sense of 'sinking' into the ground through the soles of the feet.

- Make sure that the knees do not come in front of the toes and again maintain an upright position with the body.

# ⑥ Catching a Ball

- Slowly transfer weight to the left foot and, while turning on the heel of the right foot, allow the right arm to come up in front of the body and the left to turn with the waist.

- The palms should face each other and the back should be in alignment.

# 7 Catching a Ball

- Start to transfer weight into the right foot.
- Keep the shoulders and elbows relaxed and a sense of openness between the arms and the body.
- Do not move the right knee over the toes.

# 8 Catching a Ball

- When the weight is 70 per cent on the right foot, turn the head to face the original forward position.
- Maintaining relaxed shoulders and elbows, prepare gradually to transfer the weight fully onto the right foot in preparation for stepping forward with the left.

# 9 Ward Off Left

- Place the left heel forward at a comfortable stepping distance in front.

- Ensure that there is a shoulder-distance between the feet when the forward step is taken.

- By keeping the weight-bearing knee bent, better balance will be achieved and a vertical position with the body will be maintained.

# 10 Ward Off Left

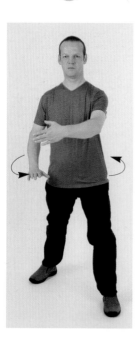

- Transfer the weight 70 per cent onto the front (left) foot.
- As weight is transferring onto the left foot, allow the body to turn from the waist to face the forward direction.
- The left arm finishes around the front of the body and the right hand should be resting by the side, palm downward.

# 11 Catching a Ball

- Start to transfer weight back to the right and turn to face the corner to the immediate left.

- As the waist is turned, allow the palms to turn to face each other at a natural distance apart.

# 12 Catching a Ball

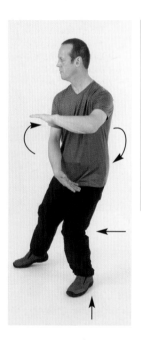

- With the weight fully on the left foot, turn the body to face forward to the right.

- Maintain contact through the ball of the right foot and keep the knees bent. This maintains a good connection with the ground before preparing to transfer weight to the right.

# 13 Ward Off Right

- Turn the body fully to face the right in preparation for transferring the weight to the right foot.
- Start to raise the right arm up in front of the chest, keeping it a comfortable distance from the body.

# 14 Ward Off Right

- Let the weight come 70 per cent onto the right foot and, as the right hand reaches chest height, let the left palm face the inside of the right wrist.

- Ensure there is a shoulder-distance between the feet. The front foot points forward while the rear foot is at a 45° angle.

# 15 Roll Back

- Staying predominantly on the right foot, turn the waist and look to the front-right direction.

- Allow the right arm to move with the waist and let the left palm come to the inside of the right elbow.

- Keep a sense of openness around the body and under the arms.

# 16 Roll Back

- Start to transfer the weight back onto the left foot until it reaches 70 per cent.
- Turn the waist so that the body faces towards the front-left.
- The arms should be guarding the centre of the body with the intention being straight forward.

# 17 Press

- Turn the body to face forward, squaring up for the press.
- Let the left palm come in contact with the inside of the right wrist in preparation for the press forward.
- The right arm should be around the front of the body at a comfortable distance.

# 18 Press

- Start to transfer the weight onto the right foot.
- Without overextending the arms, press the left palm through the right wrist.
- Let the power come from the back foot, through the transference of weight into the arms.

# 19 Open

- When 70 per cent of the weight is on the right foot, the end of the press should have been reached.

- Allow the arms to open in front of the chest but still in a position to give protection to the front of the body.

# 20 Push

- Transfer weight 70 per cent back onto the left foot.
- Keep the arms in a position that would allow a push against the chest of an opponent.
- Remember not to lock the front leg, and keep the back in alignment.

# 21 Push

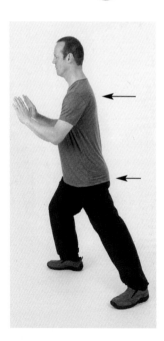

- Transfer the weight 70 per cent onto the right foot while pushing straight forward.

- Remember that the push does not come from the arms and upper body but through the back foot, up the legs, across the shoulders and through the hands.

- The power comes from the connection with the ground and the transference of weight.

# 22 Single Whip

- Let the weight gradually transfer until 70 per cent on the rear (left) foot.

- As the weight is transferred to the back foot, allow the arms to open out in front.

- Ensure that the shoulders, elbows and hands are soft and relaxed without becoming insipid and limp.

## 23 Single Whip

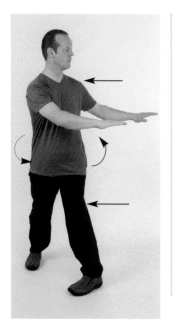

- Keeping your weight on your left foot, turn your waist around 180° to face the opposite direction.

- As you are turning the waist around, let the right foot turn to face left.

- Make sure you move from the waist and try to keep the shoulders down and relaxed.

# 24 Single Whip

- Turn the waist back 180° and let the left hand face up while the right hand closes the fingers and thumb together as if picking up a pinch of spice from the palm of the left hand.

## 25 Single Whip

- Turn the waist 90° to the left while transferring the weight to the right leg.

- At the same time extend the right arm towards the front-right corner and let the left hand rest, palm up, near to the waist.

- Do not let the left arm come too close to the body.

# 26 Single Whip

- Step back and place the left heel on the ground.
- Let the waist gradually turn around, and allow the left arm to open out from the body with the turning of the waist.

# 27 Single Whip

- As the heel comes into place, turn the left toe around to face straight ahead.
- With the turning of the waist, allow the left arm to extend in front of the centre of the body and, as the weight is gradually shifted forward, imagine transferring the energy through the palms to the chest of the opponent.

# 28 Single Whip

- Allow the weight to transfer 70 per cent onto the left foot.

- In this position the body and left foot should be facing straight forward and the right foot should be at an angle of 45°.

- Do not overextend the left arm.

# 29 Opening

- Start to transfer the weight fully onto the left foot while turning the waist slightly towards the right.

- Let the arms move as the waist moves without letting them lose a sense of moving from the centre of the body.

- Always remember that all movements come from the waist.

# **30** Play Guitar

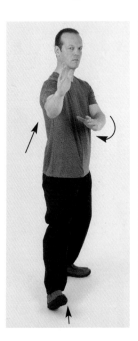

- Bring the right leg to rest, heel on the ground in front of the left.
- Most of the weight remains on the left foot, with the right merely touching the ground.
- The arms begin to come together in front of the body.
- The right hand extends forwards and upwards with the elbow remaining relaxed.
- The left palm is in front of the inside of the right elbow.

# 31 Shoulder Stroke

- Bring the right foot towards the inside of the left foot while keeping the weight on the left.
- Drop the right arm down, parallel to the right leg, while turning the body to face to the left.

# 32 Shoulder Stroke

- Transfer the weight onto the right foot until it is 70 per cent on that foot.
- Bring the right hand in to rest in front of the groin while the left hand rests on the inside of the right elbow.
- While transferring through to the right foot, imagine that something is being pushed against with the right shoulder.

# 33 White Crane Spreads Wings

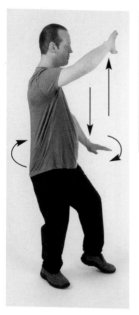

- When the weight is fully on the right leg, turn the body to face forwards.
- At the same time, let the right arm come up the front of the body and the left hand rest at the side of the left hip.

# 34 White Crane Spreads Wings

- Bring the right hand up in front of the head a little higher than the forehead and a relaxed arm's distance out.

- The weight remains fully on the right foot, with the ball of the left foot making light contact with the ground in front.

# 35 Brush Left Knee & Push

- As the waist is turned to the right, let the left arm come out to the front of the body while the right arm comes to the inside of the left elbow.

- Keep the weight on the right foot and maintain contact with the ground through the ball of the left.

# 36 Brush Left Knee & Push

- With the weight on the right foot, start to turn the waist to the right.
- Let the left hand be level with the head and the right palm beside the inside of the left elbow.
- Keep the shoulders relaxed and maintain a connection with the ground through the left toe.

# 37 Brush Left Knee & Push

- Continue to turn the waist 90° to the right.

- Keep the arms at either side on the centre of the body, protecting the central line.

- The left hand should be in the line of vision while the right hand stays, palm up, close to the left elbow.

# 38 Brush Left Knee & Push

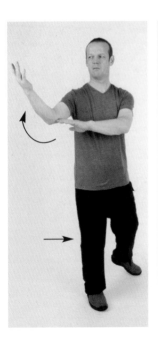

- Let the right arm come up, palm upwards.
- The weight is still predominantly on the right leg while maintaining a bent knee.
- Be sure to keep a sense of being sunk into the ground through the soles of the feet.
- Try not to let the body rise upwards.

## 39 Brush Left Knee & Push

- Turn the waist round towards the left, in preparation for transferring forward to the left foot.
- Let the right hand pass close to the ear while the left hand maintains a defence across the front of the chest.
- Keep the arms a comfortable distance from the body.

# 40 Brush Left Knee & Push

- Step out with the left foot, shoulder-distance away from the right foot, and let the left heel make contact with the ground.

- The right hand begins to sweep down as the waist is turned in preparation for pushing straight forward towards the middle of the opponent's chest.

# 41 Brush Left Knee & Push

- Start to transfer the weight onto the left foot while squaring up to the forward direction.
- The right arm comes into position as the waist turns to face the front.
- The left arm begins to come in front of the body while dropping to waist height.

# 42 Brush Left Knee & Push

- Let the weight come 70 per cent onto the left foot with the toes facing straight forward.

- As the weight is transferred onto the left foot, the body should be facing straight ahead, the right hand pushing towards the partner's chest and the left hand brushing down past the left knee.

# 43 Step Up to Play Guitar

- Step up with the right foot, bringing it level with the left.

- The weight stays mainly on the left foot while the right makes contact with the ground next to it.

- Allow the right hand to stay up while the left remains close to waist height.

# **44** Play Guitar

- Transfer the weight fully onto the right foot and step up with the left heel.
- Bring the left arm up to the front while the right arm comes to the inside of the left elbow.
- Keep a sense of protecting the central line while the arms are in an open, relaxed position.

# 45 Brush Left Knee & Push

- With the weight on the right foot, start to turn the waist to the right.
- Let the left hand be level with the head and the right palm beside the inside of the left elbow.
- Keep the shoulders relaxed and maintain a connection with the ground through the left heel.

# 46 Brush Left Knee & Push

- Let the right arm come up behind, palm upwards.
- The weight is still mostly on the right leg, while the knee stays bent.
- Be sure to keep a sense of being sunk into the ground through the soles of the feet.
- Try not to let the body rise upwards.

# 47 Brush Left Knee & Push

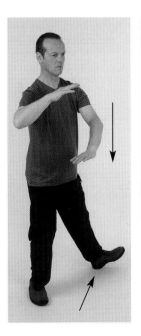

- Step out with the left foot, feet shoulder-distance apart, and let the left heel make contact with the ground.
- The left hand begins to sweep down as the waist and head are turned to the left in preparation for pushing straight forward towards the middle of the opponent's chest.

# 48 Brush Left Knee & Push

- Transfer some weight onto the left foot as you square up to the forward direction.
- The right arm comes into position as the waist turns to face the front.
- The left arm begins to come in front of the body.

# 49 Brush Left Knee & Push

- Let the weight come 70 per cent onto the left foot, with the toes facing straight forward.

- As the weight is transferred onto the left foot, the body should be facing straight ahead, the right hand pushing towards the partner's chest and the left hand brushing down past the left knee.

# 50 Step up, Parry & Punch

- Transfer the weight back onto the right foot while turning the waist slightly to the left.
- Let the right arm open in front of the body while the left arm remains near the waist, palm down.

# 51 Step Up, Parry & Punch

- Start to transfer the weight forward onto the left foot.
- Let the right arm drop down while remaining a comfortable distance from the body.
- At the same time begin to make a soft fist with the right hand.
- The left palm stays close to the left knee.

# 52 Step Up, Parry & Punch

- Step forward with the right foot, placing the heel on the ground, shoulder-distance out.
- Let the right arm turn with the fist facing up while the waist turns to the right.
- The left arm rests inside the right elbow.
- Keep the arms at either side of the central line.

# 53 Step Up, Parry & Punch

- Transfer the weight onto the right foot while maintaining contact, through the left toe, with the ground.

- Let the waist turn to the right while the fist comes to the right side of the waist.

- The left arm extends as the body turns, to create a defence in front of the central line.

# 54 Step Up, Parry & Punch

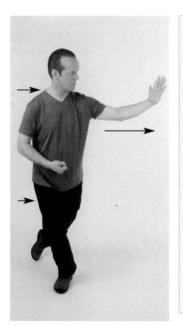

- Let the weight come fully onto the right foot in preparation for stepping forward with the left.

- The left arm extends forward while the focus is in front.

- The right fist comes to the side of the waist ready to punch forward as the weight transfers.

# 55 Step Up, Parry & Punch

- As the weight transfers onto the left, square the body up in preparation for delivering the punch to the lower abdomen.

- The left arm stays in front of the body protecting the central line.

- The left foot faces forward, and the right foot starts to turn to 45° position while the body squares up.

# 56 Step Up, Parry & Punch

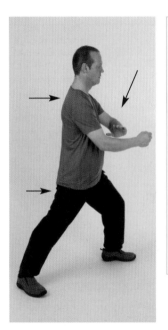

- Let the weight transfer 70 per cent to the left foot while delivering the right punch to the lower abdomen.

- The left hand rests beside the right elbow.

- The body should be in an upright position, being careful not to extend the left knee over the toes.

## 57 Withdraw

- Let the punch continue to the left as the waist is turned.

- Keeping the right arm a reasonable distance from the body, allow the left hand to drop under the right elbow as the waist is turned to the left.

# 58 Withdraw

- Allow the weight to transfer gradually back to the right foot as the arms come to cross in front of the body.
- Begin to turn the body slowly to face forward.

# 59 Push

- Prepare to turn the palms outward in order to push towards the opponent's chest.
- Have a feeling of the push coming from the ground, through the rear foot, as preparation is made to transfer the weight forward.

# 60 Push

- Turn the palms to face the front and transfer the weight forward while pushing into the opponent's chest.
- Let the weight come 70 per cent onto the left foot, taking care not to let the knee come over the toes or let the right leg lock.
- Do not extend the arms too far as the push comes from the transference of weight.

# 61 Withdraw

- Transfer the weight 70 per cent back to the right foot.
- As the weight transfers, allow the arms to extend out, being careful not to let them lock while keeping the shoulders down in a relaxed position.

# 62 Cross Hands

- Start to transfer the weight onto the left foot as the body is turned to the right.
- Let the right arm turn up, close to the head, as the body is turned.
- Be careful to keep the shoulders down.
- The left arm follows to come up in line with the right.

# 63 Cross Hands

- Turn the body fully to the right and extend the arms out to each side of the head.

- While the body is turning to the right, turn on the heel of the left foot to allow it to face forward.

- Ensure that the shoulders are relaxed and not rising up.

# 64 Cross Hands

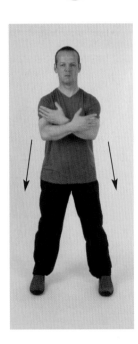

- Step back with the right foot, bringing it parallel with the left with both feet facing forward.
- Let the right arm cross over the left in front of the body, a comfortable distance from the chest.

# 65 Close

- Let the weight transfer evenly between both feet.
- Allow the arms to drop to each side and take a few moments to listen to the breathing and focus on the lower abdomen area (the dantien).

# LEARNING TAI CHI

When Tai Chi Ch'uan was developed it was built upon the foundations of martial arts and Chinese philosophy. In those times it was more important to be able to defend yourself and your family against attackers than it was to ensure a long healthy life. Today, as the art of Tai Chi Ch'uan becomes increasingly popular, it is worth considering how it fits in with today's technologically dependent society.

With the continued growth and development of technology it was once thought that people would have more leisure time in which to enjoy their lives. This is certainly not the case today. Stress levels are at their highest as people are working harder than ever. The human race is less dependent on manual labour, as much of today's technology is applied to easing physical tasks. Less manual labour means that our bodies are being exercised less through daily toil and so alternative methods of keeping physically fit and active need to be found. As people's brains become busier, through the constant demands on their time, they are allowing themselves less opportunity to quieten their minds. This results in us becoming physically unfit and mentally stressed.

Tai Chi offers space to quieten the mind and exercise the body in a gentle, undemanding way. It can be applied to a wide range of situations as an aid to relaxation and reducing stress.

Today Tai Chi is regularly taught and practised in:
- hospitals
- colleges
- council offices
- sports centres
- universities
- prisons
- mental health groups
- special needs groups
- health clubs
- commercial businesses
- senior citizens' associations

With regular practice Tai Chi is a highly effective tool that can be practised by anyone, at any time and anywhere. No special tools or clothing are needed. All that is required is yourself and a little quiet place.

# How can I learn?

In the mid-1960s one or two individuals who had visited the Far East and studied the art of Tai Chi started to teach it in the West. By the early 1970s there were probably no more than a few dozen teaching in America and Europe. The late 1970s would have seen perhaps a few hundred teachers in the West and by the mid- to late-1980s the numbers would have swelled to two or three thousand throughout the Western world. Today, in any major city of a million upwards, there will be a choice of somewhere between thirty and fifty individuals teaching Tai Chi or, as is increasingly occurring, something that they refer to as Tai Chi. The choices are many. However, by taking the time to consider the points made below, the beginner will be in a position to make a more informed choice before parting with their hard-earned cash!

## ATTENDING CLASSES

With the huge increase in interest in Tai Chi there has been a corresponding increase in the number of teachers. With a proliferation of teachers and classes it becomes increasingly difficult to know which is the right class for you to attend. The Tai Chi Union for Great Britain and the British Council for Chinese Martial Arts can supply information on registered instructors in the vast majority of regions in the UK, and the Taijiquan and Qigong Federation can advise on teachers overseas.

Many local authorities and sports clubs are including Tai Chi classes in their programmes, as are an increasing number of community-based projects and health-promotion departments. Contact the local council, library or sports centre for information. Most towns and cities are now fortunate enough to have a wide range of classes on offer. As there are so many approaches to this multifaceted art, it is often worth

*Tai Chi is taught in a wide variety of locations*

looking around before deciding which one is right for you. Here are some things to bear in mind that can help you to make the right choice of class or teacher.

## REGISTRATION

If the teacher is registered with either of the professional bodies mentioned above, they will have been subject to some degree of quality control. There may, of course, be similarly qualified instructors who have not yet registered with any organisation, for whatever reason, but it is obviously safer to place your trust in someone who has been approved by a recognised authority.

## VISIT A REGULAR CLASS

If you are lucky enough to have a choice of classes in the area, why not visit two or three before making a

*Choose a quiet place, indoors or outdoors, for practising*

final decision? Increasingly today people are looking for a class close to where they live. If they have to travel more than a few miles they lose interest in attending. Don't restrict choice by being unwilling to travel. Remember there are many aspects to this art and even more approaches to the teaching of it. Shop around and see what's on offer.

## INSTRUCTOR'S APPEARANCE

It may seem a bit harsh to judge someone on his or her external appearance. However, if one intends to invest time and energy learning a health-related discipline it would seem reasonable to expect the instructor to at least look healthy. A teacher who benefits personally from his or her practice is obviously better equipped to pass this experience on to students.

## STUDENTS

Observe the regular students as they are going through their routine. Do they have a sense of togetherness, or are they all doing the same sequence of movements in very different ways? The idea of breeding a race of Tai Chi robots is not an attractive one, but they should not be totally disjointed either. They are, after all, learning the same system.

## WHAT IS BEING TAUGHT?

If the student is primarily interested in Tai Chi as a means of relaxation, fighting applications may not be the main concern. However, if Tai Chi principles are being applied to an everyday, stressful working environment, then principles and techniques that create effective fighting applications may prove effective tools in today's competitive business world. Remember, Tai Chi deals not with force against force, but rather with neutralising the opponent's oncoming energy with softness and sensitivity.

## BOOKS

It used to be argued that a student should not buy a book on Tai Chi until he or she had studied for two years. The reason for this was that there were so many instructional books that offered confusing variations on the theme. Some left out certain moves, while others included totally different sequences. Often the applications or suggested postures conflicted with other books, and some gave only brief and confusing texts to describe complex transitions. Now there is a case for regular students to consider purchasing books with only a few photographs focusing on postures and principles rather than teaching very long sequences. At the early stages of learning it is more useful to read about how one should feel when practising and it is obviously better to learn the movements from a good teacher, rather than trying to follow photographs. However, if you can't attend a class, try practising only a short sequence and allowing the body time to get accustomed to the quality of movement.

## VIDEOS

In the early days of Tai Chi in the West, when there was only a small number of people with both the skills and the connections to make a video, the end result was often poorly presented and poorly produced. Now, as both Tai Chi and production skills improve, we are starting to see high-quality productions that contain clear, understandable instructions that can actually be followed.

For those who are unable to attend a regular class, a video can provide a good introduction to this highly rewarding art. However, in order to learn from a video you must have the willpower and discipline to work hard. The student becomes his or her own teacher, and in order to develop he or she must be a strict master. Regular practice and close attention to the movements being taught will pay dividends.

## CD-ROM

With the advent of this new technology there are many possibilities for presenting material on Tai Chi. It is easy to stop and freeze postures, and the mix of text, music, drawings, still pictures and video provides the perfect medium for learning a movement exercise.

# Tai Chi events

In addition to practising alone or attending regular classes, there are many other ways in which students can further develop their training. Throughout the UK there are regular Tai Chi competitions where one can either observe or test skills against others. In the UK and across Europe there is an ever-increasing number of Tai Chi camps and international conferences where teachers and students from all over Europe gather together to learn and share skills. These camps provide a wonderful opportunity to meet others and learn new techniques.

# Tai Chi today

Modern Tai Chi has a great number of uses and variations. This is a healthy sign, and it will help to ensure Tai Chi's long-term development. Providing what is being taught and practised adheres to a set of classic principles, it is still Tai Chi. It is limiting to pigeonhole how Tai Chi should be interpreted today. Many traditionalists despair at what they see as a watering-down of the original fighting art and many more, who see the principles being applied as practical working tools in the 21st century, approve of the use of fighting techniques. What the world has today is a strong base for further growth and development of an art that can provide untold benefits on many levels. Carefully consider what you are looking for and if you approach the Tai Chi world with an open heart and an open mind it will serve you well.

# APPENDICES

# Glossary

**Beihui point:** an acupoint at the top of the head where, according to Tai Chi theory, a person's energy connects with the heavens.

**Buddha:** Indian religious figure born in the 6th century BC. His followers believe that he rediscovered the path to enlightenment.

**Chen Style:** an often dynamic style of Tai Chi devised by the Chen family in the 17th century.

**chi:** in Chinese culture, the energy or force essential for life and contained within the meridians.

**Chi Kung:** exercises which develop and promote the flow of internal energy (chi) around the 'meridians' of the body.

**Ch'uan:** meaning 'fist' or 'boxing', the 'Ch'uan' of 'Tai Chi Ch'uan' (Tai Chi's full name) makes the art a practical one.

**Da Lui:** a short, structured set of Tai Chi movements practised by two people and based around the concept of the Eight Powers.

**Dantien:** an area just around the navel in the abdomen where, according to Tai Chi theory, the energy is stored.

**Eight Powers:** combinations of solid and broken lines which, in Eastern thought, symbolise various different kinds of flux.

**Free Pushing:** a Tai Chi exercise involving two people where each tries to overbalance the other.

**Hand Form:** a series of carefully choreographed movements performed without the use of weapons.

**I Ching:** the classic Chinese book which depicts the concept of yin and yang through the symbolism of the Eight Powers.

**meridians:** in Eastern thought, the pathways in the body along which the chi energy travels.

**Laogong point:** an energy point found in the centre of a person's palm.

**Nei Kung:** a system of 'internal' training which develops internal energy, strengthening the body.

**San Shou:** a two-person training routine based on delivering blows to various parts of the body and neutralising those of the opponent.

**Shaolin Temple:** a holy temple in China famous for its martial arts training.

**Short Yang Form:** a sequence of choreographed movements developed by the Yang family.

**Sticking Hands:** two-person training exercises whereby one partner shuts their eyes and is 'led' by the other. This develops sensitivity and awareness.

**Sun Style:** one of the five styles of Tai Chi. Characterised by short, compact movements and upright postures.

**Taoism:** a Chinese religious system based on the idea of 'going with the flow' or letting events follow their natural course.

**Thirteen Postures:** the original sequence of movements devised by Chang San-Feng from which Tai Chi was developed.

**Tui Shou or 'Push Hands':** a two-person training system for sensitivity awareness and martial application.

**Wu Style:** one of the five styles of Tai Chi. Characterised by compact, tight movements.

**Yang Style:** perhaps the most popular of the five styles of Tai Chi. Characterised by its open, expansive movements.

**yi:** intent or focus of the mind.

**yin and yang:** the concept of two opposing yet complementary forces central to the practice of Tai Chi.

**Yongquan point:** an acupoint on the centre of the sole of the foot which connects with the energy contained within the ground.

# Further information

## RECOMMENDED BOOKS

Dan Docherty, *Complete Tai Chi Ch'uan* (Crowood Press).

Wong Kiew Kit, *The Complete Book of Tai Chi Ch'uan* (Element).

As well as publications dedicated to the art of Tai Chi, your understanding of the principles and overriding concepts can be improved by looking at related Chinese subjects like *I Ching*, Chi Kung and other internal Chinese arts.

Lam Kam Chuen, *The Way of Healing* (Gaia).

James MacRitchie, *The Chi Kung Way* (Element).

Martin Palmer, *Tao Te Ching* (Element).

Michael Tse, *Qigong for Health and Vitality* (Piatkus).

Alan Watts, *Tao – The Watercourse Way* (Arkana).

## RECOMMENDED VIDEOS

Ronnie Robinson, *Tai Chi for Anyone, Anytime, Anywhere: Short Yang Form* (BMA 032).

Ronnie Robinson, *The Chi Kung Way to Health & Vitality* (BMA 031).

## RECOMMENDED CD-ROM

A. Odusanya, *Interactive Tai Chi Ch'uan* (Acu-Media Interactive Books).

# Useful addresses

Please send these organisations an SAE with any postal enquiries.

**The Tai Chi Union for Great Britain**
11 Littlemill Drive
Balmoral Gardens
Crookston
Glasgow
G53 7GF
telephone: 0141 638 2946
fax: 0141 621 1220
website: www.taichiunion.com
email: secretary@taichiunion.com

The Tai Chi Union for Great Britain has a register of over 300 qualified instructors teaching in all areas of the UK. They encompass a wide range of approaches to the art from health and relaxation to practical, effective self-defence techniques.

**The British Council for Chinese Martial Arts**
c/o 31 Neale Drive
Greasby
Wirral
Merseyside
Liverpool
L49 1SE
telephone/fax: 0151 677 4471
website: www.bccma.org.uk
email: info@www.bccma.org.uk

The British Council for Chinese Martial Arts, as its title suggests, is predominantly concerned with promoting Tai Chi C'uan as an effective martial art.

**Tai Chi & Chi Kung Forum for Health and Special Needs**
163 Palatine Road
Didsbury
Manchester
M20 2GH
website: www.taichiandspecialneeds.co.uk

**The British Open Tai Chi Ch'uan Championships**
9 Ashfield Road
London
N14 7LA

telephone: 020 8368 6815

An annual competition held in April.

**Tai Chi Caledonia**
18 Branziert Road North
Killearn
Glasgow
G63 9RF
telephone: 013552 35722
website: www.taichi-caledonia.co.uk

An international residential Tai Chi course which regularly includes many of the best-known instructors in Europe, held annually in Scotland.

**Taijiquan and Qigong Federation for Europe**
website: www.tcfe.org
email: info@tcfe.org

This organisation exists for the promotion of Taijiquan and Qigong in Europe. It stages biannual competitions and camps in different European locations.

COLLINS GEM
**1950s**
a mine of information

COLLINS GEM
**1960s**
a mine of information

COLLINS GEM
**1970s**
a mine of information

COLLINS GEM
**1980s**
a mine of information

COLLINS Jane's
**CIVIL AIRCRAFT**
a mine of information

COLLINS GEM
**CLANS & Tartans**
a mine of information

COLLINS GEM
**Classic TV SERIES**
a mine of information

COLLINS Jane's
**COMBAT AIRCRAFT**
a mine of information

COLLINS GEM
**FIRSTS**
a mine of information

COLLINS GEM
**GOLF**
a mine of information

COLLINS GEM
**HILLWALKER'S Survival Guide**
a mine of information

COLLINS GEM
**HOME EMERGENCY GUIDE**
a mine of information

COLLINS GEM
**Collecting STAMPS**
a mine of information

COLLINS GEM
**STARS**
a mine of information

COLLINS GEM
**SUPERSTITIONS**
a mine of information

COLLINS GEM
**Using Your SOFTWARE**
a mine of information